A MIDSUMMER NIGHT'S DREAM

Artists: Penko Gelev
Sotir Gelev

Editor: Stephen Haynes
Editorial Assistant: Mark Williams

Published in Great Britain in MMX by
Book House, an imprint of
The Salariya Book Company Ltd
25 Marlborough Place, Brighton, BNI IUB
www.salariya.com
www.book-house.co.uk

ISBN-13: 978-1-906714-72-7 (PB)

S A L A R I Y A

1 3 5 7 9 8 6 4 2

A CIP catalogue record for this book is available
from the British Library.

Printed and bound in China.
Printed on paper from sustainable sources.

Visit our website at **www.book-house.co.uk**
or go to **www.salariya.com** for **free** electronic versions of:
You Wouldn't Want to be an Egyptian Mummy!
You Wouldn't Want to be a Roman Gladiator!
You Wouldn't Want to be a Polar Explorer!
You Wouldn't Want to sail on a 19th-Century Whaling Ship!

Picture credits:
p. 40 Topfoto.co.uk

Every effort has been made to trace copyright holders. The Salariya Book Company apologises for any omissions and would be
pleased, in such cases, to add an acknowledgement in future editions.

GRAFFEX™

A Midsummer Night's Dream

William Shakespeare

Illustrated by

Penko Gelev

Retold by

Ian Graham

Series created and designed by

David Salariya

Ancient Greece:
The palace of Theseus,
Duke of Athens

Duke Theseus is preparing for his marriage to Hippolyta, Queen of the Amazons, a race of warrior women. There are four days to go before the wedding, and Theseus plans to fill the time with lavish entertainment.

CHARACTERS

Theseus, Duke of Athens

Hippolyta, Queen of the Amazons

Oberon, King of the Fairies

Titania, Queen of the Fairies

Puck, or Robin Goodfellow, Oberon's jester

Egeus, a nobleman

Hermia, Egeus's daughter, in love with Lysander

Demetrius, a young courtier, in love with Hermia

Lysander, a young courtier, also in love with Hermia

Helena, in love with Demetrius

Peter Quince, a carpenter

Nick Bottom, a weaver

Francis Flute, a bellows-mender

Robin Starveling, a tailor

Tom Snout, a tinker

Snug, a joiner

Philostrate, Theseus's Master of the Revels*

Peaseblossom

Cobweb

Moth

Mustardseed

Four fairies who are servants of Titania

*Master of the Revels: official in charge of court entertainments.

An Angry Visitor

Theseus's palace, Athens

Now, fair Hippolyta, our nuptial hour draws on apace.[1]

Theseus is looking forward to his wedding to Hippolyta.

Theseus won Hippolyta in battle, but he vows to marry her with great celebrations and entertainments.

Full of vexation[2] come I, with complaint against my child, my daughter Hermia.

This man hath my consent to marry her.

Egeus arrives at the palace and asks Theseus to punish his daughter for refusing to marry Demetrius.

Egeus accuses Lysander of stealing his daughter's heart.

As she is mine, I may dispose of her[3]...

What say you, Hermia? Demetrius is a worthy gentleman.

This man hath bewitched the bosom of my child.

...either to this gentleman, or to her death.

So is Lysander.

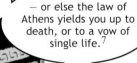

Demetrius — I'll avouch it to his head[4] — made love to[5] Nedar's daughter Helena, and won her soul.

Fit your fancies to your father's will[6] —

— or else the law of Athens yields you up to death, or to a vow of single life.[7]

I must confess that I have heard so much.

1. our nuptial hour draws on apace: our wedding approaches fast.
2. Full of vexation: Angry.   3. dispose of her: decide who is to have her.   4. I'll avouch it to his head: I'll say it to his face.
5. made love to: courted.   6. Fit . . . will: Agree to do what your father wants (marry Demetrius).   7. a vow of single life: life as a nun in a convent.

RUNNING AWAY

Lysander suggests to Hermia that they marry outside Athens, where Athenian law does not apply.

The course of true love never did run smooth.[1]

I have a widow aunt.

From Athens is her house remote seven leagues.[2]

There, gentle Hermia, may I marry thee.

Lysander asks Hermia to meet him in the wood the next night.

Steal forth[3] thy father's house tomorrow night; and in the wood, a league without[4] the town, there will I stay[5] for thee.

My good Lysander, I swear to thee... truly I will meet with thee.

Hermia agrees to run away with Lysander.

God speed fair Helena!

Call you me fair? Demetrius loves *your* fair.[6]

Were the world mine, Demetrius being bated,[7] the rest I'd give to be to you translated.[8]

O, teach me how you look, and with what art you sway the motion of Demetrius' heart.

Helena bemoans the fact that Demetrius loves Hermia and not her.

Helena would give anything to change places with Hermia. Helena asks Hermia for the secret to winning Demetrius's love.

8

1. The course of true love never did run smooth: Those who are in love always face problems.
2. remote seven leagues: seven leagues (about 35 kilometres) away.   3. Steal forth: Sneak away from.   4. without: outside.   5. stay: wait.   6. your fair: your beauty.   7. Demetrius being bated: except for Demetrius.   8. to be to you translated: to be transformed into you.

Whatever Hermia does to discourage Demetrius, he still loves her.

The more I hate, the more he follows me.

The more I love, the more he hateth me.

I frown upon him; yet he loves me still.

His folly,[1] Helena, is no fault of mine.

O that your frowns would teach my smiles such skill!

Hermia protests that she does nothing to attract Demetrius.

Take comfort: he no more shall see my face; Lysander and myself will fly this place.

Through Athens' gates have we devis'd[2] to steal.

Farewell, sweet playfellow; pray thou for us, and good luck grant thee thy Demetrius!

Lysander and Hermia tell Helena of their plan to run away.

Hermia hopes that when she leaves, Demetrius may once again love Helena.

Ere Demetrius look'd on Hermia's eyne,[3] he hail'd down oaths[4] that he was only mine.

I will go tell him of fair Hermia's flight.

Helena remembers how Demetrius loved her before he saw Hermia.

Helena plans to win Demetrius back.

1. His folly: His foolishness.   2. devis'd: planned.   3. Ere Demetrius look'd on Hermia's eyne: Before Demetrius looked into Hermia's eyes.   4. he hail'd down oaths: he swore.

THE PLAYERS MEET

Peter Quince, a carpenter, has written a play to perform for the Duke and Duchess after their wedding.

Quince explains the play to his actors, a group of tradesmen.

Nick Bottom, a weaver, is to play the male lead.

Bottom relishes the prospect of playing a lover and moving the audience to tears.

Flute the bellows-mender is unhappy to hear that he is to play a woman.[7]

Flute is relieved to hear that he can hide his face.

Bottom interrupts. He wants to play Flute's part as well as his own.

---

1. scroll: list.   2. interlude: a short play put on between other entertainments.   3. Marry: A word that means something like 'indeed' or 'now then'.   4. lamentable: very sad. Quince doesn't seem to know what 'comedy' means.
5. tyrant: cruel ruler.   6. most gallant: very bravely.   7. to play a woman: In Shakespeare's time it was normal for female characters to be played by boys.   8. monstrous little: tiny.

Robin Starveling, you must play Thisbe's mother.

Tom Snout, the tinker? You, Pyramus' father. Myself, Thisbe's father.

Snug, the joiner, you the lion's part.

Have you the lion's part written? Pray you, if it be, give it me; for I am slow of study.

You may do it extempore,[1] for it is nothing but roaring.

Snug worries about learning his lines, but there are none. All he has to do is roar.

Let me play the lion too. I will roar, that I will do any man's heart good to hear me.

You would fright the Duchess and the ladies.

I will aggravate[2] my voice so, that I will roar you as gently as any sucking dove.

You can play no part but Pyramus: for Pyramus is a sweet-faced man.

Quince tells Bottom that Pyramus is a very handsome man. Flattered, Bottom agrees to play only Pyramus.

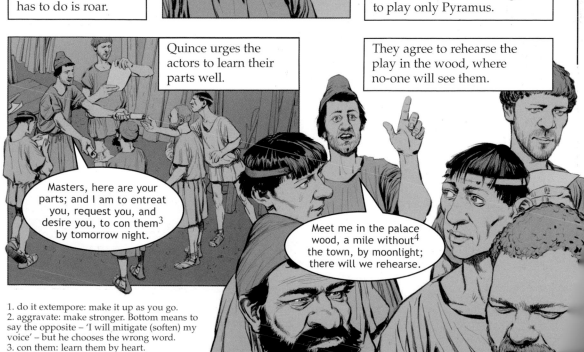

Quince urges the actors to learn their parts well.

They agree to rehearse the play in the wood, where no-one will see them.

Masters, here are your parts; and I am to entreat you, request you, and desire you, to con them[3] by tomorrow night.

Meet me in the palace wood, a mile without[4] the town, by moonlight; there will we rehearse.

1. do it extempore: make it up as you go.
2. aggravate: make stronger. Bottom means to say the opposite – 'I will mitigate (soften) my voice' – but he chooses the wrong word.
3. con them: learn them by heart.
4. without: outside.

OBERON PLOTS

Meanwhile, in the wood:

How now, spirit!

Puck, who serves Oberon, meets a fairy who serves Titania, the fairy queen.

The King doth keep his revels[1] here tonight; take heed the Queen come not within his sight.

Puck warns the fairy to keep Titania and Oberon apart, because they are bound to quarrel.

She as her attendant hath a lovely boy, stol'n from an Indian king — and jealous Oberon would have the child.

They are aguing over a servant boy.

You are that shrewd and knavish sprite[2] call'd Robin Goodfellow.

Thou speak'st aright.[3]

The fairy recognises Puck and calls him by his other name.

Ill met[4] by moonlight, proud Titania.

What, jealous Oberon!

The King and Queen of Fairies meet by chance in the wood and immediately start arguing.

Your warrior love to Theseus must be wedded.

I know thy love to Theseus.

Titania accuses Oberon of being in love with Hippolyta. Oberon accuses Titania of loving Theseus.

I do but beg a little changeling boy[5] to be my henchman.[6]

His mother was a votress[7] of my order.

But she, being mortal, of that boy did die;[8] and for her sake do I rear up her boy.

Oberon asks for the child, but Titania refuses.

Give me that boy.

Not for thy fairy kingdom.

Fairies, away!

---

12   1. keep his revels: hold a party.   2. shrewd and knavish sprite: mischievous and roguish fairy.   3. Thou speak'st aright: You are correct.   4. Ill met: You are unwelcome.   5. changeling boy: human boy stolen by the fairies. 6. henchman: page of honour.   7. votress: devoted follower.   8. of that boy did die: died giving birth to the boy.

Oberon plans his revenge on Titania.

Well, go thy way; thou shalt not from[1] this grove till I torment thee for this injury.[2]

Once I sat upon a promontory,[3] and heard a mermaid on a dolphin's back.

I remember.

Oberon reminds Puck of something he saw once.

I saw Cupid all arm'd.[4]

A certain aim he took, and loos'd his love-shaft[5] smartly from his bow.

He remembers seeing Cupid, the god of love, firing an arrow.

Fetch me that flower.

It fell upon a little western flower.

The juice of it, on sleeping eyelids laid, will make a man or woman madly dote upon[6] the next live creature that it sees.

The arrow landed on a flower.

Oberon sends Puck away to find the magic flower.

I'll put a girdle round about the earth[7] in forty minutes.

I'll watch Titania when she is asleep, and drop the liquor of it in her eyes.

Puck promises to be quick.

The next thing then she waking looks upon — she shall pursue it with the soul of love!

Oberon plans to use the juice of the magic flower on Titania.

I'll make her render up her page to me.[8]

He'll trick Titania into giving her Indian boy to him.

---

1. Thou shalt not from: You shall not leave.   2. injury: insult.   3. promontory: headland.   4. Cupid all arm'd: the god of love, armed with a bow.   5. love-shaft: Cupid's arrow, which makes its victims fall in love.   6. dote upon: fall in love with.   7. I'll put a girdle round about the earth: I'll circle the world.   8. render up her page to me: let me have her servant boy.

SEEKING HERMIA

Demetrius searches the wood for Lysander and Hermia, but can't find them.

Demetrius rejects Helena's advances.

But Helena will not be put off.

Demetrius doesn't want Helena to follow him.

Demetrius threatens to leave Helena to the wild animals in the wood.

Demetrius threatens to hurt Helena himself unless she leaves him alone.

Helena welcomes death if it is at the hand of her love, Demetrius.

1. they were stol'n unto this wood: they went unseen to this wood.   2. You draw me – for my heart is true as steel: You attract me like a magnet, as if my heart were made of steel.   3. I am your spaniel: Treat me like a pet dog.   4. fawn on you: show you great affection.   5. in my respect: in my eyes.   6. brakes: dense undergrowth.

Ere he do leave this grove[1]...

...thou shalt fly him, and he shall seek thy love.

Oberon plans to punish Demetrius for his rudeness.

Hast thou the flower there?[2]

Ay, there it is.

Puck returns with the magic flower.

I know a bank where the wild thyme blows.[3] There sleeps Titania sometime of the night.

Take thou some of it, and seek through this grove. A sweet Athenian lady is in love with a disdainful[4] youth.

Anoint[5] his eyes; but do it when the next thing he espies may be the lady.

And with the juice of this I'll streak her eyes, and make her full of hateful fantasies.

Oberon sends Puck to look for Helena.

Thou shalt know the man by the Athenian garments he hath on.

Effect it with some care,[6] that he may prove more fond on[7] her than she upon her love.

Oberon tells Puck how to recognise Demetrius by his clothes.

Fear not, my lord, your servant shall do so.

1. Ere he do leave this grove: Before he leaves this wood.   2. Hast thou the flower there?: Do you have the flower?
3. blows: flowers.   4. disdainful: scornful.   5. anoint: smear.   6. Effect it with some care: Do it carefully.
7. fond on: in love with.

LOST IN THE WOOD

The fairies sing until Titania falls asleep.

Oberon squeezes magic flower juice onto Titania's eyelids. She will love the next person she sees. Oberon hopes it will be a monster!

Lysander and Hermia stop to rest, because Lysander has forgotten the way to his aunt's house.

They lie down to sleep — not together as Lysander wishes, but apart.

Puck is still searching for Demetrius.

He mistakes Lysander and Hermia for Demetrius and Helena.

Puck squeezes some juice from the magic flower onto Lysander's eyelids.

---

1. offices: duties.   2. What thou seest when thou dost wake, do it for thy true-love take: Whatever you see when you awake, you will fall in love with it.   3. you faint: you're very tired.   4. troth: truth.   5. churl: ill-mannered person. (Puck thinks he is speaking to Demetrius, who has insulted Helena.)   6. owe: possess.

Demetrius is still trying to get away from Helena.

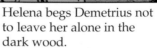

Helena begs Demetrius not to leave her alone in the dark wood.

She discovers Lysander on the ground.

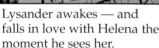

Lysander awakes — and falls in love with Helena the moment he sees her.

She thinks he is making fun of her.

Lysander, no longer in love with Hermia, leaves without her.

Hermia wakens from a nightmare. She has dreamt that a snake is attacking her.

Shocked to discover that Lysander has gone without her, she sets off to find him.

1. Do not haunt me thus: Don't hang around me all the time like this.   2. O wilt thou darkling leave me? Will you leave me in the dark?   3. You do me wrong, in such disdainful manner me to woo: You treat me badly, to pretend so cruelly that you love me.   4. serpent: snake.   5. remov'd: gone.

MAKING AN ASS OF BOTTOM

The actors meet in the wood.

Bottom voices his worries about the play.

He suggests a way to solve the play's problems – write a prologue.[3]

Snout thinks of another problem.

Someone must play the Moon...

...and the wall that keeps the lovers apart.

An actor will hold his fingers apart to make a hole that Pyramus and Thisbe can talk through.

18   1. pat: perfectly.   2. cannot abide: cannot bear. Bottom thinks the audience will be frightened, thinking the action on stage is real.   3. prologue: a speech given to an audience before a play, telling them what to expect. The actor who makes this speech is also called the Prologue.   4. device: plan.   5. afeard: afraid.   6. to present the person of Moonshine: to represent the Moon.   7. the chink of a wall: a crack in a wall.

What hempen homespuns[1] have we swaggering here?

Puck discovers the actors in the wood.

Hark,[2] a voice!

He goes but to see a noise that he heard, and is to come again.

Pyramus, played by Bottom, hears a voice offstage.

O monstrous! O strange! We are haunted!

When Bottom returns, Puck has worked mischievous magic on him!

Why do they run away? This is a knavery[3] of them to make me afeard.

I will sing, that they shall hear I am not afraid.

What angel wakes me from my flowery bed?

Titania is awakened by Bottom's singing.

I pray thee,[4] gentle mortal, sing again. I love thee!

Bewitched by the magic flower juice, she instantly falls in love with him.

Peaseblossom, Cobweb, Moth and Mustardseed!

Be kind and courteous to this gentleman.

Titania orders her fairies to look after Bottom.

1. hempen homespuns: people wearing clothes home-made from hemp; in other words, country bumpkins.
2. Hark: Listen.   3. knavery: wicked trick.   4. I pray thee: I beg you.

MISTAKEN IDENTITY

Meanwhile:

Oberon waits for news of the trick he has played on Titania.

Oberon is pleased with Puck's work.

Puck says he has used the magic flower juice on Demetrius.

But there has been a dreadful mistake...

Puck realises that he has put the magic juice on the wrong man!

1. what it was that next came in her eye: what she saw when she woke.   2. crew of patches: group of fools.
3. rude mechanicals: uneducated workmen.   4. thick-skin: brutish fellow.   5. barren: empty   6. nole: head.
7. latch'd: moistened.   8. as I did bid thee do: as I asked you to do.

Hermia suspects that Demetrius has killed Lysander out of jealousy.

Demetrius denies killing Lysander.

Hermia storms off and Demetrius lies down to sleep.

Puck must find Helena.

This time, the magic flower juice will make Demetrius love Helena.

Helena approaches, followed by Lysander.

1. rebuke: scold, tell off. 2. slain: killed. 3. stol'n away: crept away unnoticed. 4. carcass: dead body.
5. You spend . . . misprised mood: You are getting carried away by your mistaken anger. 6. vein: temper.
7. look: make sure that. 8. fond pageant: foolish antics.

RIVALS IN LOVE

Why should you think that I should woo in scorn?[1] Look, when I vow,[2] I weep.

These vows are Hermia's.

Helena refuses to believe that Lysander loves her.

Lysander says he was mistaken when he thought he loved Hermia.

I had no judgement when to her I swore.

Nor none, in my mind, now you give her o'er.

O Helen, goddess, nymph,[3] perfect, divine!

I see you all are bent[4] to set against me for your merriment.

Demetrius awakes and declares his love for Helena, but she thinks he is mocking her.

If you were civil, and knew courtesy, you would not do me thus much injury.[5]

Now neither of them is interested in Hermia.

You both are rivals, and love Hermia; and now both rivals to mock Helena.

In Hermia's love I yield you up my part.

Lysander, keep thy Hermia. If ere[6] I lov'd her, all that love is gone.

Helena scolds the two men for making fun of her.

1. in scorn: not seriously.   2. vow: promise.
3. nymph: a spirit of nature, a beautiful maiden.
4. bent: determined.
5. do me thus much injury: insult me so much.
6. ere: before.

1. yonder: over there.   2. press: force, compel.   3. engilds: decorates with gold, makes more beautiful.
4. oes and eyes of light: stars.   5. conjoin'd: banded together.   6. in spite of me: against me.
7. Ay, do, . . . hold the sweet jest up: Go on then, keep it up, keep the joke going.

LOVE AND HATE

Demetrius and Lysander both pledge their love for Helena.

They are even ready to fight over her.

Hermia tries to stop them, but Lysander is furious.

Hermia accuses Helena of stealing Lysander's love.

1. withdraw: come away. 2. burr: a seed covered with hooks that sticks to clothes and animal fur. He means that she is clinging to him and won't let go. 3. tawny Tartar: dark-skinned barbarian. In Shakespeare's time, very pale skin was fashionable. 4. Do you not jest?: Surely you're joking? 5. canker-blossom: a grub that ruins a beautiful flower.

Are you grown so high in his esteem because I am so dwarfish and so low? I am not yet so low but that my nails can reach unto thine eyes.

Good Hermia, do not be so bitter with me. Let me go.

Why, get you gone! Who is't that hinders you?[1]

A foolish heart that I leave here behind.[2]

What! with Lysander?

With Demetrius.

Only Helena's love for Demetrius stops her from leaving.

Be not afraid; she shall not harm thee, Helena.

No sir, she shall not.

Both men rush to Helena's defence.

Though she be but little, she is fierce.

'Little' again!

Hermia objects to their jokes about her height.

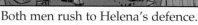

Lysander challenges Demetrius to fight over Helena.

Now follow, if thou dar'st, to try whose right, of thine or mine, is most in Helena.[3]

Your hands than mine are quicker for a fray;[4] My legs are longer, though, to run away.

I am amaz'd, and know not what to say.

1. Who is't that hinders you?: Who is it that stops you leaving? 2. A foolish heart . . . behind: According to Elizabethan poetry, when you are in love your heart stays with your loved one. 3. to try . . . Helena: to find out which of us has most right to Helena. 4. fray: fight.

KEEPING THE PEACE

Oberon isn't sure whether Puck caused the chaos by accident or design.

This is thy negligence. Still thou mistak'st — or else committ'st thy knaveries wilfully.[1]

Believe me, king of shadows,[2] I mistook.

Did not you tell me I should know the man by the Athenian garments he had on?

Puck was told to give the magic juice to an Athenian – and that's what he did.

Lead these testy[3] rivals so astray as one come not within another's way.

Now he must keep Lysander and Demetrius apart so they can't fight.

He must tire them out till they fall asleep, then use another magic herb to reverse the effect of the flower juice.

From each other look thou lead them thus...

...till o'er their brows death-counterfeiting sleep with leaden legs and batty wings doth creep.[4]

Then crush this herb into Lysander's eye.

I'll to my queen, and beg her Indian boy; and then I will her charmed eye release from monster's view, and all things shall be peace.

Meanwhile, Oberon will free Titania from her love of Bottom.

Up and down, up and down, I will lead them up and down.

Where art thou, proud Demetrius? Speak thou now.

Here, villain, drawn[5] and ready. Where art thou?

Puck confuses the lovers by mimicking their voices.

---

1. This is thy negligence . . . wilfully: This is your carelessness. You keep making mistakes – or else you played these tricks on purpose. 2. shadows: spirits. 3. testy: quarrelsome. 4. till o'er their brows . . . doth creep: until they are overcome by a deep, death-like sleep. 5. drawn: with a drawn sword.

Lysander! Thou runaway, thou coward, art thou fled?[1]

Thou coward! I'll whip thee with a rod; he is defil'd[2] that draws a sword on thee.

When I come where he calls, then he is gone.

The villain is much lighter-heel'd[3] than I.

Lysander, puzzled, gives up the chase and lies down to rest.

Come, thou gentle day. I'll find Demetrius, and revenge this spite.[4]

Ho, ho, ho! Coward, why com'st thou not?

Where art thou now?

Come hither;[5] I am here.

Shine, comforts,[6] from the east, that I may back to Athens by daylight.

Helena yearns for daybreak, to find her way back to Athens.

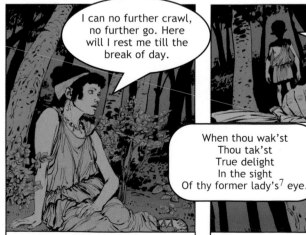

I can no further crawl, no further go. Here will I rest me till the break of day.

Hermia is exhausted.

On the ground Sleep sound; I'll apply To your eye, Gentle lover, remedy.

When thou wak'st Thou tak'st True delight In the sight Of thy former lady's[7] eye.

Puck sings as he applies the herb to Lysander's eyelids.

1. art thou fled?: have you run away?   2. defil'd: disgraced.   3. lighter-heel'd: faster.   4. spite: bad luck.
5. Come hither: Come here.   6. comforts: reassuring daylight.   7. thy former lady: the lady you loved before (Hermia).

RIGHTING WRONGS

Come sit thee down upon this flowery bed, while I thy amiable[1] cheeks do coy[2]...

Titania dotes on Bottom. She makes her fairy servants pamper him.

Ready.

Where's Peaseblossom?

...and kiss thy fair large ears, my gentle joy.

Scratch my head, Peaseblossom.

Monsieur[3] Cobweb, kill me a red-hipped humble-bee[4] and bring me the honey-bag.

Where's Monsieur Mustardseed?

Wilt thou hear some music, my sweet love?

I have a reasonable good ear in music.[7]

Ready.

Help Cavalery[5] Cobweb[6] to scratch.

Say, sweet love, what thou desir'st to eat.

Methinks I have a great desire to a bottle of hay.[8]

I have an exposition[9] of sleep come upon me.

Sleep thou, and I will wind thee in my arms. Fairies, be gone!

Bottom's tastes are those of a donkey.

---

1. amiable: lovable.   2. coy: caress, stroke.   3. Monsieur: French for 'Mr' or 'Master'.   4. humble-bee: bumblebee.
5. Cavalery: *cavaliero*, an Italian word for a sprightly military man.   6. Cobweb: Shakespeare has forgotten that it is Peaseblossom who is scratching Bottom's head.   7. good ear in music: Donkeys are famous for the unmusical sounds that they make.   8. bottle of hay: bundle of hay.   9. exposition: He means 'disposition', an inclination or tendency.

Oberon has persuaded Titania to give him the changeling…

Welcome, good Robin.[1] Seest thou this sweet sight?

When I had at my pleasure taunted her, I then did ask of her her changeling child; which straight she gave me.

…and now prepares to release her from his spell.

And now I have the boy, I will undo this hateful imperfection of her eyes.

My Oberon! What visions have I seen! Methought I was enamour'd of an ass.[2]

There lies your love.

How came these things to pass?

Robin, take off this head.

Titania thinks she has been dreaming.

Come, my queen, take hands with me…

…and rock the ground[3] whereon these sleepers be.

Oberon and Titania dance.

Tell me how it came this night that I sleeping here was found with these mortals on the ground.

Titania still has no idea what happened to her.

1. Robin: Robin Goodfellow, Puck's other name.   2. enamour'd of an ass: in love with a donkey.   3. take hands with me, and rock the ground: dance with me.

29

ALL'S WELL

Theseus and Hippolyta are hunting in the wood.

Since we have the vaward of the day,[1] my love shall hear the music of my hounds.[2]

Hippolyta tells Theseus of a hunt she enjoyed in Crete.

Never did I hear such gallant chiding.[3]

They stumble across the sleeping youths.

But soft, what nymphs are these?

I wonder of their being here together.

Egeus is puzzled to find the rival youths so close together.

No doubt they rose up early to observe the rite of May.

Egeus, is not this the day that Hermia should give answer of her choice?[4]

It is, my lord.

Go, bid the huntsmen wake them with their horns.

1. the vaward of the day: the early part of the day; the morning.   2. the music of my hounds: Elizabethans placed great importance on the 'music' of a pack when choosing hounds.   3. chiding: barking of hounds.   4. give answer of her choice: say whether she agrees to marry Demetrius, as her father wishes.

30

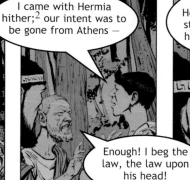

Lysander admits that he planned to run away with Hermia.

Theseus decides that the three couples will be married in one ceremony.

Demetrius is reunited with Helena. Lysander and Hermia are together again, too.

Bottom awakes, unaware that the other actors have gone.

1. concord: agreement, peace.   2. hither: to this place.   3. stealth: secret plan.   4. by and by: presently.   5. knit: married.

LOST AND FOUND

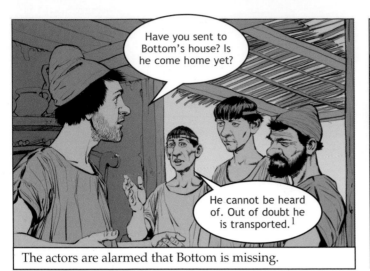

"Have you sent to Bottom's house? Is he come home yet?"

"He cannot be heard of. Out of doubt he is transported.[1]"

The actors are alarmed that Bottom is missing.

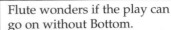

Flute wonders if the play can go on without Bottom.

"If he come not, then the play is marred:[2] it goes not forward, doth it?"

"It is not possible. You have not a man in all Athens able to discharge Pyramus but he."

"He hath simply the best wit of any handicraft man in Athens."

"Yea, and the best person[3] too; and he is a very paramour[4] for a sweet voice."

"You must say paragon. A paramour is, God bless us, a thing of naught.[5]"

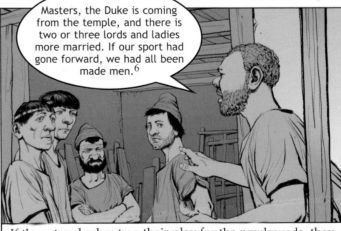

"Masters, the Duke is coming from the temple, and there is two or three lords and ladies more married. If our sport had gone forward, we had all been made men.[6]"

If the actors had put on their play for the newlyweds, they would surely have been paid a great deal of money.

1. transported: carried away, perhaps even dead.   2. marred: spoiled.   3. person: personal appearance.
4. paramour: Quince is confusing 'paramour' (lover) and 'paragon' (a perfect example of something).
5. of naught: shameful.   6. made men: wealthy men.

Panel 1:

O sweet bully[1] Bottom!

Panel 2:

Bottom bursts in, to the joy and delight of the others.

Where are these lads? Where are these hearts?[2]

Bottom! O most courageous[3] day! O most happy hour!

Panel 3:

I will tell you every thing, right as it fell out.[4]

Let us hear, sweet Bottom.

Bottom has a wonderful story to tell them – or has he?

Panel 4:

Not a word of me. All that I will tell you is, that the duke hath dined.

And, most dear actors, eat no onions nor garlic, for we are to utter sweet breath. No more words: away! Go, away!

Panel 5:

Get your apparel together, good strings[5] to your beards, new ribbons to your pumps.[6]

Meet presently[7] at the palace; every man look o'er[8] his part: for the short and the long is, our play is preferred.[9]

There is no time for Bottom's story – they must go straight to the palace to perform their play.

Bottom tells the actors to keep their breath sweet.

1. sweet bully: fine fellow.   2. hearts: good-hearted men.   3. courageous: splendid, magnificent.   4. right as it fell out: just as it happened.   5. strings: to hold their false beards on.   6. pumps: slippers.   7. presently: without delay.
8. look o'er: look over, rehearse.   9. preferred: offered to the Duke, but not yet chosen. Bottom believes it will be chosen.

THE PLAY'S THE THING

'Tis strange, my Theseus, that[1] these lovers speak of.

More strange than true. I never may believe these antique fables,[2] nor these fairy toys.

Here come the lovers, full of joy and mirth!

Theseus and Hippolyta are still puzzled by the story told by the lovers about their night in the wood.

Come now; what masques,[3] what dances shall we have?

Call Philostrate.

Here, mighty Theseus.

Theseus asks for entertainment to fill the evening.

There is a brief how many sports are ripe;[4] make choice of which your Highness will see first.

'A tedious[5] brief scene of young Pyramus and his love Thisbe, very tragical mirth'?

One of the choices is Quince's play.

No, my noble lord, it is not for you: I have heard it over, and it is nothing, nothing in the world.

We will hear it.

I will hear that play. Go bring them in.

So please your grace, the Prologue is address'd.[6]

Let him approach.

Philostrate does not recommend it.

1. that: the thing that. 2. antique fables: absurd stories. 3. masques: plays with music and dancing.
4. a brief how many sports are ripe: a list of the entertainments that are ready. 5. tedious: boring and long-winded; but the actors obviously think it means something else. 6. address'd: ready to begin.

Quince begins the prologue.

If we offend, it is with our good will, that you should think, we come not to offend, but with good will.

This fellow doth not stand upon points.[1]

A good moral, my lord: it is not enough to speak, but to speak true.

His speech was like a tangled chain: nothing impaired, but all disordered.[2] Who is next?

Gentles, perchance[3] you wonder at this show; but wonder on, till truth make all things plain.

This man is Pyramus, if you would know.

Quince prepares to introduce the characters in his play.

This beauteous lady[4] Thisbe is, certain.

This man doth present that vile Wall which did these lovers sunder[5]...

...and through Wall's chink, poor souls, they are content to whisper.

This man, with lantern, dog, and bush of thorn, presenteth Moonshine.

This grisly beast, which Lion hight[6] by name, the trusty Thisbe did affright.[7]

1. This fellow doth not stand upon points: This man doesn't follow punctuation; he doesn't pause in the right places.
2. nothing impaired, but all disordered: nothing broken, but everything out of place; he spoke the words clearly, but they did not make sense.   3. perchance: perhaps.   4. This beauteous lady: Quince promised Flute that he could wear a mask for this part (see page 10), as ancient Greek actors usually did.   5. sunder: split apart.   6. hight: is called.
7. did affright: frightened.

35

PLAY ON

Snout introduces himself to the audience.

Pyramus draws near the wall; silence!

Hippolyta is unimpressed.

1. eyne: eyes.   2. The wall . . . again: Because the wall has a mind of its own, I think it should curse him back.
3. and: if, whether,   4. Ninny's tomb: Bottom mispronounces 'Ninus' tomb' in Quince's script.
5. 'Tide life, 'tide death: whether life or death results from it.   6. discharged: carried out.   7. If we imagine no worse of them than they of themselves, they may pass for excellent men: If we think of the actors as they see themselves, then they are very good. Theseus may mean that the actors' efforts should be appreciated because they mean well.

36

Lion warns the audience how frightening he is.

You ladies, you whose gentle hearts do fear the smallest monstrous mouse that creeps on floor, may now, perchance, both quake and tremble here, when lion rough in wildest rage doth roar.

A very gentle beast, and of a good conscience.

This lantern doth the horned[1] moon present; myself the Man i' th' Moon do seem[2] to be.

The man should be put into the lantern. How is it else the Man i' the Moon?

All that I have to say is, to tell you that the lantern is the moon; I, the Man i' th' Moon.

But silence: here comes Thisbe.

This is old Ninny's tomb. Where is my love?

Thisbe can't find Pyramus at their agreed meeting place.

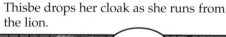

Thisbe drops her cloak as she runs from the lion.

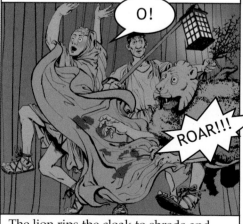

O!

ROAR!!!

The lion rips the cloak to shreds and stains it with blood from a recent kill.

Well roared, Lion!

Well run, Thisbe.

Well shone, Moon! Truly, the moon shines with a good grace.

Well moused, Lion![3]

And so the lion vanished.

1. horned: with points like horns at each end (a crescent moon).   2. seem: pretend.   3. Well moused, Lion!: Theseus compliments the lion on his treatment of the mantle as if he were cat attacking a mouse.

37

And So to Bed

Pyramus searches for Thisbe by the light of Moonshine.

Sweet Moon, I thank thee for thy sunny beams; I thank thee, Moon, for shining now so bright.

What dreadful dole[1] is here! Thy mantle[2] good, what, stain'd with blood!

He finds Thisbe's bloodstained cloak and assumes the lion has killed her.

Distraught, Pyramus draws his sword and kills himself.

Out sword, and wound the pap[3] of Pyramus; ay, that left pap, where heart doth hop.

Pyramus dies and darkness falls as Moonshine leaves.

Thus die I, thus, thus, thus. Now am I dead, now am I fled; my soul is in the sky.

How chance Moonshine is gone, before Thisbe comes back and finds her lover?

She will find him by starlight.

Hippolyta wonders how Thisbe will find Pyramus's body in the dark.

Asleep, my love? What, dead, my dove? O Pyramus, arise!

Speak, speak! Quite dumb? Dead, dead?

Thisbe kills herself with Pyramus's sword.

Farewell, friends; Thus Thisbe ends: Adieu, adieu, adieu!

Moonshine and Lion are left to bury the dead.

Ay, and Wall too.

1. dole: grief.   2. mantle: cloak.   3. pap: breast.

Will it please you to see the epilogue,[1] or to hear a Bergomask dance?[2]

No epilogue, I pray you, for your play needs no excuse.

But come, your Bergomask!

The clock strikes midnight.

The iron tongue[3] of midnight hath told[4] twelve. Lovers, to bed.

'Tis almost fairy time...

I am sent with broom before to sweep the dust behind the door.

Now that everyone is asleep, Puck arrives in the palace.

Through the house give glimmering light by the dead and drowsy fire; every elf and fairy sprite hop as light as bird from briar.

Hand in hand, with fairy grace, will we sing, and bless this place.

To the best bride-bed will we, which by us shall blessed be. So shall all the couples three ever true in loving be.

If we shadows have offended, think but this, and all is mended: that you have but slumber'd here while these visions did appear.[5]

So, good night unto you all. Give me your hands,[6] if we be friends, and Robin shall restore amends.[7]

1. epilogue: a speech to the audience at the end of a play.   2. Bergomask dance: a comic dance in the style of the people of Bergamo in Italy, ridiculed in Shakespeare's time for their rural simplicity.   3. iron tongue: the clapper that strikes the bell of the clock.   4. told: counted.   5. If we shadows . . . appear: If you didn't enjoy the play, just imagine that it was a dream.   6. Give me your hands: applaud.   7. restore amends: make amends in return.

The end 39

Willliam Shakespeare was born and brought up in Stratford-upon-Avon, a small town in Warwickshire, England. The date of his birth is not known, but he was baptised on 26 April 1564. Infant mortality was so high at that time that children were usually baptised within three days of birth, so he was probably born on or about 23 April. His father, John, was a glove-maker and wool trader. William was his parents' third child, but the first to survive to adulthood.

Shakespeare was probably educated at a local grammar school, but there is no record of him attending university. On 29 November 1582 he married Anne Hathaway. He was 18 years old. She was 26 and already expecting their first child, Susanna. They had two more children, twins called Hamnet and Judith. Sadly, Hamnet died in 1596, aged only 11. Susanna and Judith outlived their father.

Shakespeare disappeared from the historical record between 1585 and 1592. These are often called his 'lost years'. No-one knows when, or why, he left Stratford, but he reappeared in London in 1592 working as an actor and playwright. His plays were being performed at several London theatres. It isn't known how he got started as an actor or playwright.

LICENSED PLAYERS

Shakespeare belonged to London's leading theatrical company, the Lord Chamberlain's Men, and wrote most of his plays for them. At that time, troupes of players had to be licensed. They were supported financially by important

Portrait of Shakespeare by Martin Droeshout, on the title-page of the First Folio edition of Shakespeare's plays (London, 1623)

people. The Lord Chamberlain's Men were supported by Henry Carey, the Lord Chamberlain. They played mainly at the Theatre and later at the Globe. (The Theatre was the first playhouse in London – at that time 'theatre' was not an everyday word.)

By 1594, Shakespeare was part-owner of the Lord Chamberlain's Men and so he received part of their profits. He continued acting too. By 1597 he was wealthy enough to buy a large house, called New Place, in Stratford. By 1599 he was living in Southwark on the south bank of the River Thames, close to the newly built Globe theatre. His wife and family stayed in Stratford.

THE KING'S MEN

When Queen Elizabeth I died in 1603, the new king, James I, adopted the Lord Chamberlain's Men, who changed their name to the King's Men. The next year, Shakespeare moved to new lodgings north of the river. In 1608, the King's Men leased the Blackfriars playhouse, an indoor theatre. They played in the open-air Globe during the summer and in the roofed Blackfriars playhouse in the winter.

In 1613 Shakespeare bought his first property in London, a priory gatehouse in Blackfriars. He also stopped writing at about this time. He had written about 39 plays (experts disagree about the exact number), four long poems and 154 sonnets (short poems of 14 lines). His last plays were co-written with John Fletcher, who succeeded him as playwright for the King's Men.

LATER YEARS

By now Shakespeare was spending more time in Stratford, where he died on 23 April 1616, at the age of 52. He was buried in Holy Trinity Church in Stratford. His will, written just a month before his death, left most of his estate to the male heirs of his daughter, Susanna. He famously left his 'second-best' bed to his widow, Anne. Shakespeare's last direct descendant was his granddaughter, Lady Elizabeth Barnard, who died in 1670.

Only about half of Shakespeare's plays were published during his lifetime, but in 1623 a book of 36 of his plays was published. This is known as the First Folio. Since then, William Shakespeare has come to be regarded as the greatest playwright in the English language. He is often called the Bard (poet) of Avon.

Patrons arrive at the Globe theatre.

Shakespeare had the good fortune to be working as an actor and writer at a time when the first theatres were being built in London. Until the sixteenth century, plays were performed by travelling troupes of players in palaces, the grand houses of the nobility, public buildings and inn yards. Inn yards were very popular places for watching plays. The leading companies of actors were based at inns and performed their plays in the yard.

The first purpose-built playhouse in London was the Theatre. It was built in 1576 in a part of London called Shoreditch by actor-manager James Burbage. Like many early theatres, the Theatre was located just outside the boundary of the City of London, the historic centre of London. The City's authorities disapproved of theatrical performances. By building outside the City, theatre owners placed themselves beyond the reach of the City authorities.

A PENNY TO STAND

The Theatre was a wooden building with three galleries surrounding an open yard, with a stage on one side – similar to an inn yard. Customers paid a penny to stand in the cobbled yard to watch plays. Those in the galleries had to pay twopence.

The Theatre came to a strange end. When the lease on the land it stood on ran out in 1597, there was a dispute about the renewal of the lease. At Christmas 1598, the Theatre's owners solved the problem by dismantling the building, moving all the materials across the River Thames to Southwark on the south bank, and using them to build a new theatre. They named their new building the Globe. To raise the money needed to meet the cost of this new building, the owners sold shares in its ownership to the actors' company. William Shakespeare was one of four members who bought a share. The Globe opened early in 1599.

Many of Shakespeare's plays were performed at the Globe over the next 14 years. Then, on 29 June 1613, a cannon fired during a performance of Shakespeare's play *All Is True* (later renamed *Henry VIII*) peppered the theatre's thatched roof with smouldering wadding. The theatre caught fire and burned to the ground.

A new Globe theatre was built, with a tiled roof, on the same site. It thrived until all theatres were closed by England's Puritan (strict Christian) government in 1642. About two years later, it was demolished to make way for housing. In 1989 the foundations of the Globe were rediscovered underneath a car park. They revealed a 20-sided building, 30 metres across.

THE GLOBE TODAY

In 1970 the American actor, producer and director Sam Wanamaker founded the Shakespeare Globe Trust, with the aim of rebuilding the Globe theatre. After being the driving force behind the project for the next 23 years, Wanamaker sadly died before he could see the project completed. 'Shakespeare's Globe Theatre' opened in 1997, a short distance from the site of the original Globe. After 400 years, Shakespeare's plays are once again being performed at the Globe theatre.

London's Elizabethan and Jacobean theatres

NAME	DATE	LOCATION
THE THEATRE	1576	SHOREDITCH
THE CURTAIN	1577	SHOREDITCH
NEWINGTON BUTTS	1579	SOUTHWARK
THE ROSE	1587	SOUTHWARK
THE SWAN	1595	SOUTHWARK
THE GLOBE	1599	SOUTHWARK
THE FORTUNE	1600	FINSBURY
THE RED BULL	1605	CLERKENWELL
BLACKFRIARS	1608	CITY OF LONDON
THE HOPE	1613	SOUTHWARK

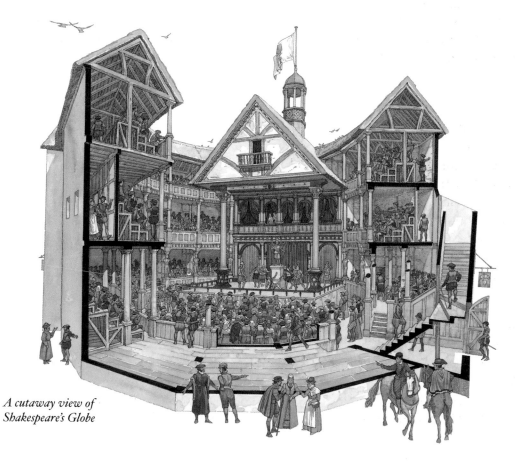

A cutaway view of Shakespeare's Globe

Many Elizabethans believed in fairies and were well acquainted with fairy folklore. However, Shakespeare changed our view of fairies forever.

In Shakespeare's time it was generally believed that fairies were the same size and shape as humans. In the play, Oberon, Puck and Titania are human-sized, but Shakespeare also describes some of his fairies as tiny winged creatures, small enough to hide in acorn cups. This is the first known appearance in English literature of small winged fairies. This image of fairies was taken up by other writers and artists and handed down the generations to the present day.

Elizabethans feared fairies, because they were thought to have magical powers that they could use to reward or punish people. As long as humans kept the fairies happy, all would be well. They might even be rewarded with good luck or by having their diseases cured. But those who angered the fairies could expect punishment. Fairies were known to pinch people who displeased them. They could also cause sickness and blight crops.

Fairies were said to enjoy music and dancing. Ring-shaped marks in grass, known as 'fairy rings', are now known to be caused by a fungus, but they were once thought to be caused by fairies dancing in a circle.

Elizabethans were familiar with Oberon, the King of the Fairies, but Shakespeare invented Titania, the Fairy Queen. He probably took her name from *Metamorphoses*, a magical poem about the creation and history of the world by the ancient Roman poet Ovid. The story of Pyramus and Thisbe also comes from *Metamorphoses*.

'Kill me a red-hipped humble-bee...' (see page 28)

For generations of children, Arthur Rackham's illustrations to a 1908 edition of A Midsummer Night's Dream *were the perfect idea of what fairies should be like.*

ROBIN GOODFELLOW

Elizabethans were familiar with a supernatural figure called Robin Goodfellow. He was a mischievous spirit who played jokes on people. Accidents were sometimes blamed on him. He is often shown in illustrations with a broom, because he rewarded people who pleased him by cleaning their houses. Shakespeare's character Puck is Robin Goodfellow by another name. True to his character, he appears at the end of *A Midsummer Night's Dream* with a broom and sweeps up the dust.

1564
William Shakespeare born in Stratford-upon-Avon, Warwickshire. Elizabeth I has ruled England since 1558.

1577
Francis Drake sets out to sail around the world on the *Golden Hind* (returns 1580).

1582
Shakespeare marries Anne Hathaway.

1583
Shakespeare's daughter Susanna born.

1585
Shakespeare's twins, Hamnet and Judith, born.

1586
English courtier, poet and military commander, Sir Philip Sidney, killed in Battle of Zutphen in the Netherlands.

1587
Mary, Queen of Scots, convicted of plotting against Elizabeth I, is executed at Fotheringhay Castle. Drake destroys Spanish ships in Cádiz harbour, Spain, and claims to have 'singed the king of Spain's beard'.

1588
Philip II of Spain launches an unsuccessful invasion of England with his 'Invincible Armada'.

1592
Earliest known reference to Shakespeare as a playwright in London.

1594
Shakespeare is now a leader of the theatre company, the Lord Chamberlain's Men.

1596
Shakespeare's only son, Hamnet, dies. *A Midsummer Night's Dream* is written at about this time.

1597
Shakespeare buys and restores New Place in Stratford.

1599
The Globe theatre opens in Southwark, where Shakespeare now lives.

1600
The future King Charles I of England is born. The first quarto edition of *A Midsummer Night's Dream* is published.

1603
Queen Elizabeth I dies, aged 69. James VI of Scotland becomes James I of England. The Lord Chamberlain's Men become the King's Men.

1605
The Gunpowder Plot, a conspiracy to assassinate James I and his Parliament, is foiled on 5 November.

1606
James's eldest son, Prince Henry Frederick, becomes Prince of Wales.

1612
Henry, Prince of Wales dies, aged 18.

1613
The Globe burns down during a performance of Shakespeare's play *All is True* (later called *Henry VIII*). It is quickly rebuilt.

1616
William Shakespeare dies in Stratford on 23 April at the age of 52.

The first performance of *A Midsummer Night's Dream* probably occurred in 1595 or 1596, shortly after it was written. The first publication of the play's script in 1600 announced that it had already been 'sundry times publickly acted'.

In 1642 the Puritan government of England closed all the theatres in London and they remained closed until Charles II came to the throne in 1660. Acting troupes got round the ban on performing plays by performing short excerpts of plays, called 'playlets' or 'drolls'. In the case of *A Midsummer Night's Dream*, the Pyramus and Thisbe part of the play was performed on its own.

A Midsummer Night's Dream was almost completely restored to its original form in 1840 at Covent Garden theatre, London, by British actress and theatre manager Madame Lucia Vestris. Madame Vestris played the part of Oberon, thus beginning a tradition of women playing Oberon (and also Puck) that lasted until the early years of the twentieth century. The Vestris production also set a trend for presenting the play as a great spectacle with music, ballet and large casts of up to a hundred players.

In 1914, an actor and director called Harley Granville-Barker restored the play to its original form. His versions of this and other plays, without grand sets, elaborate musical scores or dancers, changed the way Shakespeare's plays were performed from then on.

A PLAY IN A BOX

Peter Brook's production of *A Midsummer Night's Dream* in 1970 set new standards. He set the play within a bare white box. The fairies were portrayed as circus performers swinging on ropes and trapezes. The same actor played both Theseus and Oberon, and the same actress played both Hippolyta and Titania, to suggest that the world of the fairies was a mirror image of the real world. Brook's production encouraged later directors to try their own innovative and creative ways of telling the story of *A Midsummer Night's Dream*.

MIDSUMMER MUSIC

The English composer Henry Purcell composed *The Fairy-Queen*, a musical adaptation of *A Midsummer Night's Dream*, in 1692. Sadly, it contains none of Shakespeare's original text! German composers Felix Mendelssohn and Carl Orff wrote music for theatrical productions of the play in the mid-1800s and mid-1900s respectively. Mendelssohn's version includes the famous Wedding March which was used for the marriage of Queen Victoria's daughter and is still popular today. Benjamin Britten's opera based on the play was performed for the first time in 1960. In 1997 Steve Hackett, who had been a guitarist with the rock band Genesis in the 1970s, wrote a musical version of the play, accompanied by the Royal Philharmonic Orchestra.

MOVIE DREAMS

A Midsummer Night's Dream has been filmed on many occasions. Some are straightforward adaptations for the big screen, while others are more loosely based on Shakespeare's play. The earliest is a 12-minute silent film dating from 1909. Here are just a few of the best-known.

1935: *A Midsummer Night's Dream* (USA)
A well-received and glamorous Hollywood version based on a Broadway play, starring Olivia de Havilland as Titania and James Cagney – better known for his gangster roles – as Bottom.

1968: *A Midsummer Night's Dream* (UK)
A Royal Shakespeare Company film directed by Peter Hall and starring Judi Dench as Titania.

1999: *Midsummer* (USA)
A modern setting of the play, written for the screen, produced and directed by James Kerwin.

1999: *A Midsummer Night's Dream* (USA)
An adaptation set in Tuscany, Italy, in the nineteenth century, starring Michelle Pfeiffer as Titania and Kevin Kline as Bottom.

2001: *The Children's Midsummer Night's Dream* (UK)
A film of the play performed by children.

2001: *Get Over It* (USA)
A loose adaptation set in a modern high school, starring Kirsten Dunst.

'I will sing, that they shall hear I am not afraid.' (see page 19)

Bottom transformed, as imagined by Arthur Rackham in 1908

IF YOU ENJOYED THIS BOOK, YOU MIGHT LIKE
TO TRY THESE OTHER GRAFFEX TITLES:

Adventures of Huckleberry Finn Mark Twain

Beowulf

Dr Jekyll and Mr Hyde Robert Louis Stevenson

Dracula Bram Stoker

Frankenstein Mary Shelley

Gulliver's Travels Jonathan Swift

Hamlet William Shakespeare

The Hunchback of Notre Dame Victor Hugo

Jane Eyre Charlotte Brontë

Journey to the Centre of the Earth Jules Verne

Julius Caesar William Shakespeare

Kidnapped Robert Louis Stevenson

The Last of the Mohicans James Fenimore Cooper

Macbeth William Shakespeare

The Merchant of Venice William Shakespeare

The Man in the Iron Mask Alexandre Dumas

Moby-Dick Herman Melville

The Odyssey Homer

Oliver Twist Charles Dickens

Romeo and Juliet William Shakespeare

A Tale of Two Cities Charles Dickens

The Three Musketeers Alexandre Dumas

Treasure Island Robert Louis Stevenson

Twenty Thousand Leagues Under the Sea Jules Verne

Wuthering Heights Emily Brontë